# The Virtuous

What is a weed? A plant whose virtues have not yet been discovered.

*Ralph Waldo Emerson*

# The Virtuous Weed

*Garnered by* Joy Griffith-Jones

*Blond & Briggs*

*What right have you, O passer-by-the-way*
*to call any flower a weed?*
*Do you know its merits, its virtues,*
*its healing qualities?*
*Because a thing is common*
*shall you despise it?*

Illustrations from
*The Herball or Generall History of Plants*
by John Gerard 1597

*for Susan and Sheila*
*and other "passers-by-the-way"*

First published in Great Britain 1977
by Blond & Briggs Ltd, London and Tiptree,
Colchester, Essex.
Designed by Humphrey Stone and
Printed in Great Britain by
The Compton Press Ltd, The Old Brewery
Tisbury, Salisbury, Wilts
in Linotype Granjon
on Design Cartridge
© copyright 1977 Joy Griffith-Jones
Reprinted 1978

ISBN 85634 079 0

# *Foreword*

The more we learn about nature the more we must doubt our theories. Evolution, for instance, claims that what exists today is through natural selection, that nature is a utilitarian system allowing survival only to the fittest as if designed by the engineers of a multi-national corporation. This view obscures the marvels of nature which is an artistic wonder, infinitely playful, subtle and inventive, whose wisdom we should be humbly eager to understand.

Alas, we approach nature in a very different spirit, as a system that requires continuous correction. How incompetent she is, allowing pests and diseases, iron to rust, useful substances to decay, and low parasites to flourish at the expense of higher creatures. All this has to be battled with. Cosmic incompetence has produced friends and enemies for us and once we know who is who, we know what to do – kill the enemy.

Among the enemies are weeds, useless and troublesome plants in cultivated land, springing up where not wanted. The multi-national corporation called nature has failed to develop effective weed-killers, but our own multi-nationals have succeeded where nature has failed. We can exterminate the weeds . . .

But do we really know what we are doing? Is this a matter for killing, or thoughtful, gentle, loving management? Is there really no virtue in weeds? Are they really unmanageable, so that there is no alternative to *herbicide*?

Let us study them, as our ancestors have done with science *and* sensitivity, and learn from nature. We can start, where we may expect the least, but can find enough for a lifetime, in our own backyard, with *The Virtuous Weed*.

E. F. SCHUMACHER

# Agrimony

Agrimonia eupatoria
Church steeples
Cockeburr
Sticklewort
Philanthropos

'It is an herb under Jupiter and the sign Cancer and strengthens these parts under the Planet and sign, and removes diseases in them by sympathy; and those under Saturn, Mars and Mercury by anti-pathy; if they happen in any part of the body governed by Jupiter or under the signs of Cancer, Sagittary or Pisces and there, must needs be good for the gout . . ."

The Ancients called it *Philanthropos* on account of its beneficial properties. One of them suggested that it should be taken 'with a mixture of pounded frogs and human blood as a remedy for internal haemorrhages'

Agrimony tea is drunk on the Continent for its fragrance as well as for its virtues as a spring tonic and for cleansing the system

An infusion makes an excellent gargle for colds and a relaxed throat

Considered useful in drawing out splinters of wood, thorns 'or any such thing in the flesh'

'A decoction of leaves is good for them that have naughty livers'

## *Bluebell*

Hyacinthus nonscriptus
Auld man's bells
Culverkeys
Ring-o'-bells
Jacinth
Wood bells

Found in woods, by the roadside, on hedgebanks
and in meadows

The names and spellings of flowers have gone
through many changes over the years. Shakespeare's
'azured harebell' refers to our bluebell

Often known as Wild Hyacinth, named after
Hyacinthus who was accidentally killed by Apollo.
Traditionally, considered a flower of grief and
mourning

The bulb contains diuretic, balsamic and styptic
qualities

The sap from the bluebell was used as a gum in the
Middle Ages to fix the feathers to the shaft of an
arrow. Its sticky properties were used as a substitute
for starch and as a bookbinders' gum

It is Ben Johnson's 'fair haired hyacinth'

'The Harebell for her stainless azured hue
claims to be worn of none but those who are true'

*William Brown*

# Burdock

Arctium lappa
Fox's clote
Lappa
Beggar's buttons
Love leaves
Personata
Clot-bur

A plant that adapts itself to all kinds of soil and is found on waste ground, around old buildings, by the roadside and in fairly damp places, though seldom in Scotland

One of the most valued plants in herbal medicines, rich in vitamins and minerals, especially iron, and used medicinally as a diuretic and blood cleanser

The young stems, when the outer peel has been stripped off, can be boiled and served with butter and lemon juice. They have a very delicate flavour and can also be chopped and added to salads

To benefit from the mineral salts contained in the plant, the roots should be bruised and sliced, then boil 1 oz. of root with ¾ pint of water and simmer for 15 minutes. Allow to steep then drink half a cupful warmed and sweetened with honey, night and morning

'The seed being drunk in wine forty days together, doth wonderfully help the sciatica'   *Culpeper*

A lotion made from the root is used as a remedy for baldness

# Buttercup

Ranunculus bulbosis
St Anthony's turnip
Crowfoot
Goldcup
Cuckoo buds

'A fiery and hot-spirited herb of Mars'

'Abundant are the sorts of this herb, that to describe them all would tire the patience of Socrates himself'

Bulbosis refers to the bulb-like swelling at the base of the stem. Old country folk would say 'Beware St Anthony's turnip'. It is a very greedy plant and will rob neighbouring plants of nutrients in the soil. Rich in copper

Farmers used to rub the cows' udders with buttercups on May Day to increase their yield

On Midsummer's Eve the cows were garlanded with buttercup chains to bless the milk

In olden times, virgins used to make powder from this plant to furrow bridal beds

Because it possesses the property of inflaming and blistering the skin, beggars in Europe sometimes used it to cause open sores thus arousing the sympathy of passers-by

# Greater Celandine

Chelidonium majus
Garden celandine
Common celandine
Swallow wort
Tetterwort

'This is a herb of the sun and under the celestial
Leo, and is one of the best cures for the eyes for all
that know anything in astrology know that the
eyes are subject to the luminaries'

Found in waste places, in rubble and old walls, by
the roadside and in the hedgerows

It flowers when the swallows arrive and dies when
they leave

This plant possesses poisonous properties so is not
a plant to be used by the layman

A drug plant of the Middle Ages used externally for
eye ailments, warts and as a remedy against jaundice

The stems when crushed or broken produce an
orange-coloured juice with a most disagreeable
smell, staining the hands and yielding a natural dye

'It tooke that name from swallowes that cured their
young ones eyes, that were hurt, with bringing this
herb and putting it to them'

## Lesser Celandine

Ranunculus ficaria
Figwort
Smallwort
Pilewort

'It is under the dominion of Mars, and behold here another verification of the learnings of the Ancients, viz, that the virtue of an herb may be known by its signature as plainly as appears in this; for if you dig up the root of it you shall perceive the perfect image of the disease which they commonly call the piles'

No relation to the Greater Celandine but a member of the buttercup family with the same propensity for robbing neighbouring plants of nutrients. Disliked by cattle but wood pigeons appear to enjoy it

Found in hedgerows, fields and damp places and thrives beneath the shade of trees

The blossoms shut before a shower of rain, even in fine weather; they do not open much before nine in the morning and shut by five every evening

A favourite flower of Wordsworth, who refers to it as having 'a glittering countenance . . .'

A decoction made from pulped leaves mixed with a little cold cream will give relief to sufferers from piles and will often cure the trouble

# Chicory

Chichorium intybus
Succory
Blue sailors
Our Lady's eyes

Found mainly on light soils and on gravel and chalk, on waste land, the borders of fields and by the roadside. A very deep rooting plant and consequently rich in minerals and trace elements. Used in herbal leys for these properties

All blooms close by early afternoon however sunny the day. Linnaeus used chicory as one of the flowers in his floral clock at Upsala because of the regularity of its opening and closing

To be eaten boiled, or dried, roasted and added to coffee, or as a substitute for coffee. The roots can be blanched in the autumn for their delicious chicons

Chicory is the 'friend of the liver' having tonic, diuretic, depurative and laxative properties. Very helpful in gout and in rheumatic complaints

An infusion of the leaves can be used for those suffering from skin ailments

It is said to have the power to render the possessor invisible and shares with moonwort the power to open locked boxes if a leaf is held against the lock

'A fine, cleansing, jovial plant'

# Chickweed

Stellaris media
Star weed
Star chickweed
Chick wittles
Passerina

'It is a fine, soft, pleasing herb under the dominion of the Moon'

Very rich in minerals and trace elements essential in our diet, especially phosphorus, potassium, copper and iron

The plant multiplies both by seed and vegetative reproduction, and since it produces many flowers a day for several weeks, it can scatter over two thousand seeds during its lifetime

A very good example of the 'sleep of the plants'. The flowers open at nine in the morning and remain open for twelve hours in bright weather. At night, the leaves join and fold over the buds of the new shoots to protect them

An excellent and nutritious addition to salads, or cooked gently like spinach and served with a little butter

Chickweed water is an old wives' remedy for obesity

This plant has great healing properties and is used by herbalists in ointment form. Also used in the treatment of eye, liver, lung, rheumatic and skin complaints

# Cinquefoil

Potentilla reptans
Five fingers
Five-leaf grass

'This is an herb of Jupiter and therefore strengthens the part of the body it rules'

Spreads quickly by runners – like the strawberry. Rich in calcium, iron and magnesium

The flowers close completely at night and partly during dull weather

The whole plant has curative properties and is known as 'the powerful little one'. Used as a nerve sedative and general astringent

A tea made from the plant makes a good mouth-wash or gargle for sore throats. The same lotion can be used to clear the skin of pimples and soothe sun-burn

This is a plant of ancient witchcraft used in love divinations and as a remedy to keep witches and evil spirits at bay

'The juice drank, about four ounces at a time, for certain days together, cureth the quinsy and yellow jaundice, and taken for 30 days, cureth the falling sickness'

# Cleavers

Galium aparine
Goosegrass
Catchweed
Clivers
Hayruff
Robin-run-in-the-grass
Love man
Little sweethearts

'It is under the dominion of the Moon'

The stalks and leaves are covered with little hooked bristles which are used to cling to neighbouring plants to climb up and reach the sunlight. It also clings to animals and people as they pass, using them to broadcast its seeds

This is a plant very rich in minerals, especially silica, calcium and sodium and so is good for the hair and teeth. The leaves should be finely chopped and infused in hot milk. Take a tablespoon before meals

Has been used as a poultice to reduce tumours, to treat skin cancer and as a diuretic

Animals eat it and geese are especially fond of it

The stems have been used to make a rough sieve

The roots produce a red dye

'A pottage made of Cleavers, a little mutton and oatmeal is good to cause lankness and keepe from fatness'

# Red Clover

Trifolium pratense
Trefoil
Purple clover

'Mercury has dominion over this plant'

Found in meadows, by the wayside, and in gardens, preferring a light sandy soil

Frequently an indicator of a shortage of nitrogen in the soil. Use the tops in the compost heap but leave the roots in the ground to give a free dressing of nitrogen

The three leaves of the plant are considered a sign of divine powers. The Ancients called it 'God's greatest blessing to mankind'

A great strengthener of the heart and cherisher of the spirits with extraordinary healing powers. 'Defends the heart against noisome vapours of the spleen'

The flowers have been used by herbalists in the treatment of cancer

Try the flower heads in salads, or making a tea with them. This is an old remedy for whooping cough, asthma and bronchitis

A four-leaved clover hidden in the cowshed protected the cows from magic and ensured that the butter would come easily

'Trefoil, Johnswort, Vervain and Dill
hinder witches at their will'

## Coltsfoot

Tussilago farfara
Ass's foot
Coughwort
Daywort
Foalswort

'The plant is under Venus'

It is found by the wayside, in the hedgerows, waste land and meadows and especially in heavy soil

One of the best sub-soiling plants with a creeping rootstock, usually indicating a soil in need of aeration and drainage

A plant rich in minerals and trace elements, especially calcium, copper, iron, magnesium, potassium and sulphur

Called 'the son before the father' because the flowers appear before the leaves

An infusion of leaves in boiling water and sweetened with honey is an effective remedy for coughs, colds, asthma and bronchitis

The flowers were painted above the door of a pharmacist's shop in France to indicate his profession

The silky hairs of the seeds are often used by goldfinches to line their nests

'It helpeth St Anthony's fire, and burnings, and is singular good to take away wheals and small pushes that arise through heat'

# *Cornflower*

Centaurea cyanus
Blue bottle
Hurt sickle
Bachelor's buttons

'As they are naturally cold, dry and binding so are
they under the dominion of Saturn'

Found in cornfields and meadows and often by the
wayside

This plant will never grow in the company of peas
or beans

A plant highly rated by herbalists as an eye remedy
and in nervous diseases. It was said that the corn-
flower should be used for blue eyes and the
plantain for brown

An infusion can be used as a mouthwash and as a
skin lotion

It was once used as an ingredient in ink, since it
produces a beautiful blue dye

Cyanos, a Greek poet who sang of the beauty of
the earth and its riches, was changed into a corn-
flower after his death, by the goddess Flora

'Thou blunt'st the very reaper's sickle and so
in life and death becomes the farmer's foe'

# Couch Grass

Agropyron repens
Twitch
Witch grass
Dog grass
Scotch quelch

'Tis under the dominion of Jupiter and is the most medicinal of all the quick grasses'

The plant has a creeping underground stem, preferring light soil, and has been used to bind the sand together on the dunes, the roots forming a mat

A rich source of potassium, silica, and other minerals

Herbalists used the roots of this plant to relieve rheumatism and gout, and a tea made from them is effective in the treatment of cystitis

Makes a good spring tonic for the system to purify the blood, and being a diuretic has been used to reduce stones in the kidney

Dogs and cats seek it out when they are sick, eating it to make them vomit, and many other animals, both domestic and wild, seek it out for medicinal purposes

In Italy and France the roots are harvested and sold in the markets

'. . . although a gardener be of another opinion, yet a physician holds half an acre of them to be worth five acres of carrots twice told over . . .' *Culpeper*

## *Daisy*

Bellis perennis
Day's eye
Bairnwort
Bruisewort

'This daisy is governed by Venus in the sign Cancer'

Their appearance in the lawn very often indicates a
need for liming. Daisies are full of calcium and as
they die and decompose they return this calcium to
the soil: Nature's way of restoring the balance

The plant contains a very acrid secretion disliked
by insects so a mild insect repellent spray can be
made from it

Herbalists used it in the Middle Ages to treat
varicose veins and it has a reputation as a cure for
fresh wounds and 'all kinds of pains and aches'

Daisy water is said by the gypsies to cure a red nose
or red blotches on the face

'Girls who weave a daisy chain
grow up pretty never plain'

A plant that closes its eyes at night and opens them
in the morning

'That blissful sighte softeneth al my sorwe'  *Chaucer*

'There with fantastic garlands did she come
of crowflowers, nettles, daisies'

*Shakespeare, of Ophelia's garland*

# Dandelion

Taraxacum officinale
Shepherd's clock
Pissenlit – in France
Monk's head
Wet-a-bed

A most valuable plant. Very rich in mineral salts and vitamins. It is especially high in Vitamin A and contains more C than lettuce, more iron than spinach and is full of potassium, calcium, silica and magnesium

An excellent diuretic and capable of stimulating the whole system, but especially the kidneys and bladder. The juice was used to treat warts and clear pimples. A plant associated with the 'doctrine of signatures' being of an intense yellow and used in the treatment of jaundice

A plant which gives off ethylene gas which may affect the growth of neighbouring plants

The leaves are delicious in salads. Blanch them for a couple of weeks beforehand to make them less bitter. Or cook the leaves like spinach and serve them with a little butter and lemon juice. The roots dried, roasted and ground make an excellent substitute for coffee and can also be added to ordinary coffee. Dandelion wine is made from the petals only and as well as being a delicious drink, it retains the most curative properties of the plant. Excellent for the overweight who need to reduce

# *White Dead Nettle*

Lamium album
Archangels
Bee-nettle
Sucky sue
Bumble-bee flower

'The chief use of them is for women, it being an herb of Venus'

A most valuable plant for the gardener, the whole plant breaking down into almost perfect humus. Rich in minerals and trace elements and a useful addition to the compost heap

The flowers are full of nectar so this is a plant beloved by bees and other honey loving insects

Often called Adam-and-Eve because when the flower is held upside down, the black and gold stamens, side by side, look like two people asleep

The leaves cooked like spinach with a little butter and seasoning make an excellent spring tonic

Along with stinging nettles they can be made into beer

An infusion made from this plant and sweetened with honey is a good remedy for a chill

The seeds are scattered in the garden by ants who seek them out for the oil that covers them

The dried stems make good whistles

## Devil's Bit Scabious

Succisa pratensis
Ofbit
Premorse scabious

'Mercury owns this plant'

Usually found in meadows and the borders of woodland, in heaths and grassy places

A plant thought to be so useful to mankind that the devil bit off the end of the root hoping to kill it

Especially good in female ailments and for epilepsy

Rich in mineral salts, especially iron, sodium and magnesium. Brew the flowers in a pint of water and take a tablespoonful night and morning

The small, daisy-shaped flowers smell strongly of honey

'. . . to pluck it will cause the devil to appear at your bedside at night . . .'

# Common Broadleaved Dock

Rumex obtusifolius
Wayside dock
Butterdock

Found growing freely by the roadside, in the hedge-rows, on waste ground, in the meadows and our gardens

A very deep-rooting plant usually indicating a need for aeration and drainage in the soil. The roots go down nearly three feet so it is a plant rich in minerals and trace elements, especially iron. Add the leaves to the compost but leave the roots in the ground to do the job they are there for – opening up and aerating the soil

Usually found growing near stinging nettles. A very cooling plant, used to relieve nettle stings, poison ivy and other skin inflammations

The cool leaves were often used to wrap the butter in to take to market

The plant is purgative and the roots very astringent

The gypsies put the seeds of dock in a bag and tied it under the left arm as a charm against pain

The leaves can be used as a vegetable but they are extremely bitter

'When bairns' fingers nettles find
see old dock is close behind'

# Fat Hen

Chenopodium album
Frost blight
Goosefoot
Mydden miles
Lamb's quarters
Dirty Dick

'It is under the dominion of Mercury'

Usually found growing on old manure heaps, hence the country names. It also grows abundantly by the wayside and meadows near villages since it was once cultivated as a pot herb. It indicates a good soil, but one that is tired of growing potatoes

A plant of great importance, its former name was Allgood. Rich in mineral salts and containing more iron, calcium, protein and vitamins $B_1$ and $B_2$ than most cultivated vegetables

The most popular wild plant to be eaten today having a taste similar to that of Spinach. Wash well and put into a pan with some butter and a very little water. Drain, chop the leaves and return to the pan with some butter, seasoning and garlic

The seeds formed part of the last meal of the Tollund man whose remains were so perfectly preserved in peat that the stomach contents could be analysed

The plant is cultivated in Canada as a food for pigs and sheep and is said to fatten poultry

# Feverfew

Chrysanthemum parthenium
Bachelor's buttons
Devil daisy
Featherfew
Nosebleed
Headache plant

'Venus commands this herb, and has commended it to succour her sisters'

Often indicates poor soil but grows profusely, arrives uninvited and spreads like mad

Feverfew is a corruption of 'febrifuge' from its fever-reducing and tonic properties. Relieves headaches and migraine '. . . the herb being bruised and applied to the head . . .'

A very aromatic herb and important in female ailments; it used to be known as the midwives' standby

Once planted around the houses to purify the atmosphere and ward off disease

The plant is disliked by many insects, especially bees, because of its rather strong and bitter smell. To keep off flies and other insects, infuse the leaves in boiling water, cool, then sponge the skin

'The powder of the herb taken in wine, with some oxmel, purges both choler and phlegm, and is available for those that are short-winded and are troubled with melancholy and heaviness, or sadness of spirits'

# *Fumitory*

Fumaria officinalis
Earth smoke
Beggary
Fumus
Vapor

'Saturn owns this herb and presents it to the world as a cure for his own disease, and strengthener of the part of the body he rules'

Found by the wayside, near hedges and walls and thrives in ploughed fields and gardens; can be troublesome on light soils

Insects seldom visit this plant; it is self-fertile

Ants seek out the seeds for their oily coats and in this way help to scatter them around the garden and other places

Gypsies hold this plant in high regard, its chief value being in the treatment of liver ailments, as a remedy for jaundice and as an infusion for skin diseases

Used in France and Germany as a blood purifier

'Now, let it be known to all whom it may concern, that the infusion of the above described plant is said to be an excellent specific for removing the freckles and clearing the skin . . .'

# Ground Elder

Aegopodium podagraria
Goutweed
Bishopsweed
Dog Elder
Garden plague
Herb Gerard

A plant associated with monasteries, abbeys and churches

Believed to have been introduced into this country by the Romans for its ability to relieve gout; and cultivated by the monks in the Middle Ages as a herb of healing

Dedicated to St Gerard who was formerly invoked to cure the gout, against which disease the plant was used, and from which bishops seemed to suffer a good deal

A kidney-flushing herb and a sedative when taken as a tea

The young leaves make a tasty vegetable if cooked in butter with a very little water and some seasoning

Groweth of itself in the gardens without setting or sowing and is so fruitful in its increase that when it hath once taken roots it will hardly be gotten out againe, spoiling and getting every yeare more ground, to the annoying of better herbes'

# Groundsel

Senecio vulgaris
Birdseed
Ragwort
Grundy swallow
Ground glutton

'Groundsel is under the dominion of Venus and though common has many virtues'

An indicator of soil fertility according to its growth. In a poor soil it will only grow two or three inches, in a good fertile soil the plant will grow to two feet.

A mineral rich plant and a valuable source of iron with definite medicinal uses. A cooling herb, mildly purgative and diuretic, once used as a poultice for ulcers and tumours and is said to have been used successfully in cancerous conditions

Cage birds love it and the leaves and seeds are food for many wild birds. Groundsel will tempt a rabbit to eat when other food is refused

Fresh roots sniffed when first taken out of the ground are a cure for many forms of headache, but do not use a tool with iron in it on this plant

'. . . It helpeth the King's evil and the leaves stamped and strained into milk and drunk helpeth the red gums and frets in children . . .'

'The flower of this plant hath white hair and when the wind bloweth it away, then it appears like a bald-headed man'

# *Heartsease*

Viola tricolor
Wild pansy
Love-in-idleness
Love-lies-bleeding
Three-faces-under-a-hood
Herb Trinitatus
Jack-jump-and-kiss-me

'This herb is really Saturnine, something cold, viscous and slimy'

Dedicated by the Ancients to the Trinity because the flowers have three colours – Herb Trinitatus

The flowers were considered an excellent remedy for disease of the heart, hence 'Heartsease'. Belongs to the 'doctrine of signatures'

Employed as a tonic for cleansing the blood, in skin diseases, as a depurative and as a diuretic

It was used by witches and sorcerers for its potency in love charms

It is the flower which Puck was told to find by Oberon and which caused Queen Titania to become 'enamoured of an ass'

'Fetch me that flower, the herb I showed thee once; the juice of it on sleeping eyelids laid, will make a man or woman madly dote upon the next live creature that it sees'

The plant protects its flower head from rain by dropping its head in wet weather

## Hedge Garlic

Alliaria petiolata
Jack-by-the-hedge
Sauce alone
Garlic mustard
Poor man's mustard

'It is an herb of Mercury'

A very common wayside weed found under the hedges, by the wayside and in the garden

A very important food plant for the orange tip butterflies; the females lay their eggs on this plant

The leaves can be cooked like spinach but they are rather bitter

The plant gives off a strong smell of garlic when picked or bruised. Country people used the plant in sandwiches, salads and in sauces, hence the name 'sauce alone'. Especially good as a sauce with lamb, a leaf or two chopped and added to mint sauce

The plant contains antiseptic properties. A syrup of garlic is a remedy for asthma

Sniffed into the nostrils it will revive a hysterical sufferer

'The seed bruised and boiled in wine is a good remedy for the wind, colic or the stone, if drank warm'

# Henbane

Hyoscyamus niger
Hog's bean
Henbell
Jupiter's bean
Cassilago
Symphonica

'This herb is under the dominion of Saturn'

The plant has a strong and unpleasant smell and an acrid taste. It yields a drug which can be very poisonous if misused. It is an anti-spasmodic, a hypnotic and mild diuretic

It was used as a general sedative before the discovery of anaesthesia. Its medicinal use dates from a very early age; Dioscorides used it to procure sleep and allay pains

Bathing the feet in henbane before going to bed was said to be a cure for insomnia

Witches used it in their spells and love charms, and the leaves were used in sorcerers' ointments

The dead in Hades were said to be crowned with Henbane as they wandered beside the Styx

'Take notice, that this herb must never be taken inwardly; outwardly an oil, ointment or plaister of it is most admirable for the gout'

## Horsetail

Equisetum arvense
Shave-grass
Bottle-brush
Paddock pipes
Pewterwort
Meadow pine
Cat's tail

Often indicates an underground spring or water course, and sometimes a need for drainage in the garden. Usually found on heavy soil; one of the oldest plants on earth

It can make an effective spray against fungal diseases. Put two good handfuls of the plant in a pan, cover with water and simmer for twenty minutes. Cover, cool and infuse for 24 hours. Strain and dilute 2 parts of water to 1 of liquid

A mineral-rich plant, especially calcium and cobalt, and probably the richest source of silica

It has been used to stop bleeding and contains antiseptic and disinfectant properties. 'It will heal sinews though they be cut in sunder'

A valuable plant in the treatment of nervous dis-orders and can be taken as a tea to strengthen hair, nails and teeth

It was used to scour milk pails, pots and pans and pewter vessels, and fletchers and comb makers rubbed and polished their goods with it

## Lady's Smock

Cardamine pratensis
Cuckoo flower
Milkmaids
Pigeon's eye
Lady's smile
Lady's glove

'This herb is under the dominion of the Moon, good for the scurvy, provoke urine, break the stone and effectively warm an cold and weak stomach'

A member of the cabbage family and a buttercress, and found mainly in damp places

The young leaves can be used in salads or sandwiches

A plant full of vitamin C

An important food plant for the orange tip butterfly

The flowers are usually at their best when the cuckoo arrives in April, hence the country name

It is a plant of the fairies and unlucky to have in the house

'. . . and lady-smocks all silver white'

# *Mallow*

Malva sylvestris
Fairy cheeses
Pancake plant
**Rags and tatters**
Billy buttons
Flibberty gibbet

'All the Mallows are under the dominion of Venus'

Very handsome early in the summer but as time goes on the leaves becomes somewhat ragged, hence the country name

All members of this very large family of Mallows are important medicinally, and is one of the most beneficial known to herbalists

The flowers and leaves have a high mucilage content and are rich in vitamins A, B1, B2, and C. An emollient is made from them to treat inflammation of the respiratory, gastric and urinary tracts

The juice of the leaves will soothe bee or wasp stings

Pythagoras believed it to be good for 'moderating the passions and clearing the stomach and mind'

Because of the glutinous content of the leaves they are best when added to soups or stews

The seeds or 'cheeses' are eaten by country children

'When boiled in water, the strong decoction is good if drank, to provoke urine, take off the strangury, sharp humours of the bowels, and the gravel'

# Marsh Mallow

Althea officinalis
Mallards
Mauls
Mortification root

A very common roadside plant and found in waste places, salty marshes along the sea shore, and damp areas, and in farms and gardens

The young leaves are highly tonic and good eaten raw in a salad. The roots were at one time used to make marshmallow confectionery; a dish of marsh-mallows was considered a delicacy amongst the Romans

'The leaves, bruised and laid to the eyes with a little honey, takes away the imposthumations of them'

The roots contain a sweet-tasting mucilage with healing and lubricating powers. Boiled in milk and sweetened with honey it will relieve whooping cough

The roots were once used to check mortification (gangrene)

An excellent poultice can be made for boils and abscesses by pouring boiling water on to the leaves and squeezing them out in a cloth before applying to the affected part

'Whosoever shall take a spoonful of the Mallows shall that day be free from all diseases that may come to him' *Pliny*

## *Mouse-Ear Hawkweed*

Hieracium pilosella
Hawkweed
Pilosella
Mouse-ear

Found in pastures and near grazing stock, by the roadside on sunny banks and on waste land

An example of: 'Where the hurt shall bring you woe God made the healing herb'

The watery extract of this plant makes an effective remedy for infectious abortion in cattle and is often found growing near to where they graze. Also a remedy for undulant fever in humans

'To him that hath a flux, of Shepherd's purse he
                                        gives,
and Mouse-ear unto him whom some sharp rupture
                                        grieves'

Considered a good remedy for whooping cough and all lung ailments

It is still collected and used by herbalists for its medicinal properties

If mouse-ear be given to any horse 'it will cause that he shall not be hurt by the smith that shooeth him'

'Hawkweed is cooling, somewhat drying and binding, and good for the heat of the stomach and gnawings therein'

# *Plantain*

Plantago major
Englishman's foot
Ratstail
Snakeweed
Ripple grass
Waybread

A plant rich in minerals, especially potassium,
calcium and sulphur and contains the blood-clotting
vitamin K. For this reason a major wound herb and
a favourite remedy of gypsies everywhere who
peddled plantain ointment as a general cure-all

The fresh juice gives speedy relief when applied to
all manner of stings and bites from ants to dogs, and
will stop bleeding in minor cuts and grazes

It has been used as a soothing poultice and in the
treatment of syphilis

The Saxons bound it to their heads to cure a headache

The leaves can be cooked like spinach or added to
soups and stews

The tea has a tonic and diuretic effect

Called 'slan-us' in the Highlands, meaning 'a plant
of healing'

The seeds are often scattered by goldfinches

'A plant nobody should despise'

# Wild Red Poppy

Papaver rhoeas
Blind eyes
Canker
Cheesebowls
Poppet
Redweed
Sleepy head

'This herb is Lunar'

A gently narcotic plant with silvery green leaves and
drooping flower heads of an intense red. It has a
rich scent of opium when fresh which disappears
when dried. Visited by bees for its abundant pollen

All parts except the root, are medicinal. The leaves
can be used in tea and the petals for the throat and
pectoral areas. An ancient cough remedy

The highly tonic seed capsules contain pain-relieving
properties and are often sprinkled on bread, cakes
and buns – Turkish peasants make tonic cakes from
roasted poppy seeds, mixed with oil and honey and
bound with a little roasted flour

It is cultivated in parts of Germany and Flanders
for the oil obtained from the seeds

The syrup has been used as a colouring matter for
old ink

'The plant of sleep because of its opium content,
The plant of fertility because of its seeds'

# Shepherd's Purse

Capsella bursa pastoris
Lady's purse
Hen-and-chickens
Money-bags
Pepper-and-salt
Pick-pocket

'It is under the dominion of Saturn and of a cold, dry and biting nature'

A writer in the time of Louis XV said 'Old walls and tumbledown cottages are covered with this plant which multiplies marvellously'

A very aromatic plant with a peculiar and rather disagreeable smell, but considered by herbalists to be one of the best specifics for stopping haemorrhages. Rich in calcium, sodium and sulphur and contains the blood-clotting vitamin K

Chaffinches and other wild birds eat the seeds and they are a valuable food for caged birds

A plant visited by bees and other insects, but it self-pollinates before the flowers open

A mildly diuretic tea can be made from the leaves, or, when young, they can be chopped and added to salads

'The juice dropped into the ears, heals the pains, noise, and matterings thereof'

# Silverweed

Potentilla anserina
Prince's feathers
Bread-and-butter
Goose tansy
Wild agrimony
Golden sovereigns
Moor grass –in Scotland

'This plant is under Venus and deserves to be universally known in medicine'

It thrives in moist conditions and is often an indicator of a soil in need of drainage, a poor plant in dry and sandy soil. With its beautiful silvery feathery leaves and yellow flowers, often used in flower arrangements

Recognised in olden days as a source of food and cultivated for its roots which were boiled, roasted or ground into flour

A strong infusion of silverweed will check the bleeding of piles. An infusion sweetened with honey can be taken for a sore throat, and the distilled water of the plant was used to remove freckles, spots and pimples and all traces of sunburn

The leaves soothe hot, tired feet

'. . . it is good to dissipate contusions, fastens loose teeth, and heals wounds or ulcers in the mouth . . .'

# Germander Speedwell

Veronica chamaedrys
Fluellin the male
Paul's betony
Eye of Christ
Angel's eyes
Farewell
Goodbye

'Venus governs this plant and it is among the vulnery plants used both outwardly and inwardly'

This is the commonest species of speedwell and found wild on waste land, by the roadside, in the hedgerows and in the meadows

A purifier of the blood and a remedy for various skin diseases

An infusion of the plant made into a syrup with honey has been used for coughs and in the treatment of catarrh and asthma

The leaves and flowers can be made into a lotion to clear the skin of spots and pimples

The seeds are an especially good food for birds

Ants carry the seeds around often bringing them into the garden

Gerard recommends this plant for cancer, '. . . given in good broth of a hen'

# Stinging Nettle

Urtica dioica
Devil's leaf
Naughty-man's-plaything

A plant of many virtues to the gardener. Creates heat almost immediately when added to the compost heap, and can be used as a mulch. A companion to soft fruit and herbs. Nettles soaked in rainwater for a couple of weeks will produce an excellent plant food. The same liquid, strained before use, can be used as an insect repellent spray against blackfly and greenfly

Nettle tea has many uses. Taken daily it is a good tonic and will get rid of spots and pimples; the same lotion will soothe nettle rash, minor stings and burns, and sunburn

The juice of the nettle is an antidote for its own sting

Young leaves are delicious when cooked like spinach. No other green vegetable excels the nettle in minerals and vitamin content, it is one of the most chlorophyll-rich plants

'In Scotland I have eaten nettles, I have slept in nettle sheets and I have dined off a nettle tablecloth. The young and tender nettle is an excellent potherb. The stalks of old nettles are as good as flax for making cloth' *Campbell*

The seeds 'taken in a draught of wine, they arouse desire'

## *Stonecrop*

Sedum acre
Wall pepper
Prick madam
Trip madam
Welcome-home-husband-though-never-so-drunk
Wall ginger
Bird bread
Jack-of-the-buttery

'This plant is under the dominion of the Moon cold in quality, and somewhat binding, very good to stay defluxions, especially as fall on the eyes'

Grows freely on walls and cottage roofs and on rocks and sandy places

There is some controversy as to the virtues of this plant. The Ancients consider it to possess considerable properties, but Culpeper says: 'It's qualities are directly opposite to the other sedums, and more apt to raise inflammations than to cure them'

It is considered an effective vermifuge

The juice of the plant is a gypsy remedy for stings, corns and warts

'As a means of procuring sleep, it must be wrapped in a black cloth and placed under the pillow of the patient, without his knowing it, otherwise it will not be effectual'

# Vervain

Verbena officinalis
Herb of Grace
Herbe Sacree
Herba veneris

'This is an herb of Venus and excellent for the womb to strengthen and remedy all the cold distempers of it, as plantain does the hot'

It is supposed to have been discovered on the Mount of Calvary where it was used to staunch the wounds of Christ

The virtue attributed to it by the Ancients was aphrodisiacal with the power of reviving a dying love

An excellent diuretic, it is used as a remedy for kidney and liver complaints, for fevers and for poor digestion. An infusion used to bathe the forehead will soothe a headache

It was thought to be good for the eyesight

Bruised and worn round the neck it was said to be a charm against headaches and all manner of venomous bites

'Vervaine is an opener of obstructions, clenseth and healeth . . . all the inward paines and torments of the body . . . it is held also to be no lesse effectuall against all poyson, and the venome of dangerous beastes and serpents, as also against bewitched drinkes or the like . . .' *Parkinson*

## Wild Garlic

Allium ursinum
Ramsons
Stinkers
Gypsy's onions
Badger's flowers

One of our most beautiful wild plants and found in damp woodlands and pastures, releasing an unmistakable smell of garlic when pulled or trodden on

A plant rich in versatile oil and sulphur

A very powerful antiseptic acting on the mucous membranes and the bloodstream, and giving relief in asthma

Has been used to expel worms in animals and humans

Universally regarded as both healing and aphrodisiacal

It is said to draw moles from the ground and inspire cocks to fight

Stock relish it but when eaten by cattle can affect the milk. When eaten by sheep or lambs it improves the flavour of the meat

The plant can be used to flavour sauces, soups, stews and casseroles

'It is very useful in obstruction of the kidneys and dropsies, especially in that which is called anasarca'

## Wild Thyme

Thymus serpyllum
Mother of thyme
Serpyllum

'This plant is under Venus and is excellent for nervous disorders'

A very aromatic plant with tiny flat, dark-green leaves and minute pale purple flowers with a sweet and pungent smell beloved by bees

The plant contains powerful antiseptic properties yielding an essential oil, thymol, now used in modern disinfectants, hair lotions and toothpowders

Tea made from wild thyme, either by itself or with other herbs, makes an excellent remedy for headaches and other nervous ailments. It is aromatic, stimulant, antiseptic, antispasmodic, diuretic and emmenagogue

An infusion sweetened with honey is good for sore throats and coughs. Thyme tea helps in any chest complaint which causes difficulty in breathing, especially asthma

Wherever it grows the plant denotes a pure atmosphere

'. . . a strong tea makes a certain remedy for that troublesome complaint, the night-mare . . .'

Wild thyme is one of the plants needed to make a magic brew to enable one to see the fairies.